CW00382834

THE TIMES DIARY

CARTOONS

BARRY FANTONI

Anthony Blond

First published in Great Britain in 1984 by
Anthony Blond

Anthony Blond is an imprint of Muller, Blond &
White Limited, 55/57 Great Ormond Street,
London, WC1N 3HZ.

British Library Cataloguing in Publication Data

Fantoni, Barry
   The Times diary cartoons.
   1. English wit and humor, Pictorial
   I. Title
   741.5′942   NC1479

   ISBN O 85634 188 6

Printed and bound in Great Britain by
R. J. Acford, Chichester, Sussex.

"You heard. I wanna glue-sniffing
kit"

WAS MY YEAR YOUR YEAR?

The selection of cartoons in this volume begins roughly with Mrs Thatcher's return to Downing Street. In spite of the election-hogging headlines, thanks to the Great British Eccentric Spirit, there were plenty of stories to keep us amused through those serious weeks. Much mirth was engendered by the publication of "Hitler's Diaries", and much outrage by the topless goings-on at the Devon seaside resort of Torbay. Once the Tories had been re-elected we were all brought down to earth when the Tory right wing once again insisted on a debate on capital punishment. Once again the motion was heavily defeated.

Silly season

The summer, instead of bringing the traditional silly season, was highlighted by the sexploits of a head master and his wife at the select Dartington Hall school. And a top Yorkshire Ripper case detective aroused much unfavourable criticism by selling his memoirs for a fat fee. In October large numbers of Maze prisoners walked out through the main gate without permission. And at the end of October large numbers of U.S. marines walked onto the tiny island of Grenada without permission. Both events caused grave concern in high places.

● **There was even graver concern in November when a justice of the peace was found guilty of smuggling scotch and ciggies. And by the same token, Windscale was charged with depositing nuclear waste onto our shores and beaches. The judge resigned and Windscale changed its name.**

Mixed emotions

The Greenham women remain with us, arousing our divided opinions of either admiration or condemnation. Mark Thatcher, who everyone was accusing of benefiting from nepotism in Oman, is now in America, where many feel Cruise missiles should be. But if the Greenham ladies aroused mixed emotions, the two lady day trippers from Jersey won all our hearts for sheer bravado when they attempted to enter the country with hundreds of gold coins stuffed in their knickers.

Bumper year

In spite of the recession, auction houses had a bumper year. An early German volume went under the hammer for a record breaking £2 million. But my favourite story was the meeting in Poland of their Nobel Peace Prize winner, Lech Walesa, and Watford Football Club's pop singing chairman. What did they talk about? Watching Watford's dismal Wembley performance, I realised for the first time why Elton John has lost so much hair.

B.E.F

For Tesse and J.R.M.

THE
CARTOONS

"I hope that means that if we don't
like her election manifesto we'll be
able to take it back and change it"

"The bidding is against you, sir, at
twelve o'clock high"

"I do hope, Tamsin, this doesn't
herald yet another Sixties revival"

"Of course I've nothing to declare. I
don't work here"

"I'll never be much of an historian.
I find it so hard changing my mind"

"Gerald can't make up his mind
about nuclear weapons so he's
decided to vote Labour"

"Who said you can't fool all the people all the time?"

"Legs higher, back straight,
teeth clenched"

"Anything you say will be taken
down and used in my memoirs"

"Geoffrey's in a dilemma – he's given up smoking but he's in favour of hanging"

"In the old days you had to be in a
West End play to do this in public"

"Next thing, the Tory right wing will
demand the abolition of seat belts"

"Cheer up, you can't help agreeing
with Mrs Thatcher at least once"

"Amanda's dying to go, but
won't admit she's old enough to
remember them"

"I'd like to see some bloke tell me to
go and get my hair cut"

"Rest assured, Madam, all our
minks are fed on non-protected
species"

"I'm not sure, I think it says further
government cuts in education"

"Apparently you buy them in
bunches"

"Alas, I'd hoped for the part of
man selling tickets at the door"

"Not too long in the sun, Neville:
we're off to the Dordogne on
Saturday"

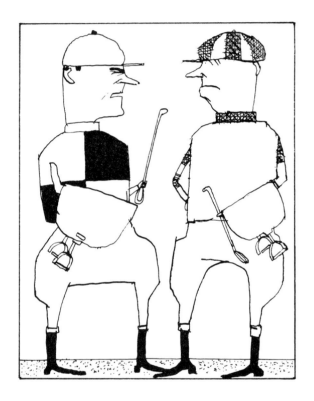

"I'm carrying five hundred pounds
in this race. How about you?"

"Curious how Gillian's Neville has
started using a public call box"

"Lucky them. Ours plays in goal"

"Gerald's so brave. He picked up
our old ironing board and just threw
it on the tip"

"Good news, dear. Pandora's
been expelled"

"They could always sell the name to a
cheese manufacturer"

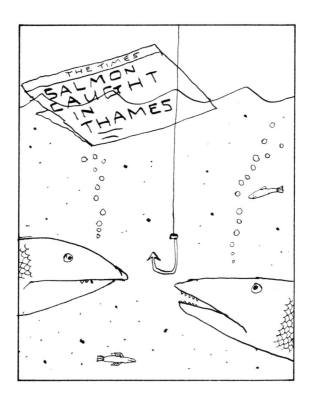

"Personally, I preferred pollution"

"This has a delightful nose with just a
hint of the Guildford bypass"

"It's to bring it in line with
smaller congregations"

"Have you any of the supergrass one
hears so much about?"

"Chase the Anstruther's cat once more
and you'll be 2,500,001"

"Done a nice job on your bill,
squire. Too bad about the car"

"Must be a result of the F-Plan Diet"

"Don't bother, I'll let myself out"

"Here are the air tickets and
insurance, and your code name's
Albatross"

"Haven't you got any wholemeal?"

"Any other experience apart from
Clacton and Filey?"

"Sorry, mein Herr, the tree
is closed today"

"Do you think we could really sell
800 million copies to the GLC?"

"If it's Thursday it must be Grenada"

"Say, what's this cricket everyone
keeps saying it ain't?"

"I got arrested for kerb-crawling"

"I hear poor old Anstruther got very
badly mauled"

"The deterrent of ex-communication,
my son, is quite different from
its use"

"The last time I asked, you said
your sales conference was in
Bradford"

"If you missed the film, Larry,
there's always the live show"

"I saw one, but it wasn't nearly as
nasty as the Falklands war"

"They fell off the back of a bench"

"Arthur's decorating the Christmas
tree. Have you got any more of that
cod that glows in the dark?"

"We're renaming it
Dunourownconveyancin"

"Nigel's furious. The fake he bid for
has turned out to be an original"

"Yes, dear, it means Mummy will
be home for Christmas"

"I'm 97 – what would I want with
long-life milk?"

"I'm delighted so long as she
doesn't wear her diamond rings
when milking"

"At least he didn't get lost
in the desert"

"Don't tell Slugger – he's got
a weak heart"

"Hullo, Houston control – I've just
been mugged"

"These are very sturdy, madam. We
call them our Jersey day trippers"

"Kidney donor card, sir? That'll do
nicely"

"Do you think they'll find enough
people with a job?"

"He might be working, he might not:
with Anstruther it's hard to tell"

"It's an odd feeling, Beryl, standing
here where our lounge used to be"

"My dad's sort of in the air force,
too – he's a flying picket"

"My husband's in the attic – Graham
Greene spent a week here just after
the war"

"At least it will save them
time training to be marksmen"

"Waddya mean, you'll complain
about me to the captain? I am
the captain"

"Terrible. I asked for a hot dog
and all I got was a sausage"

"Who's that chap with the droopy
moustache next to Elton John?"

"If it takes one minister three days to earn £265, how long does it take a teacher to get an extra seven and a half per cent?"

"Do you suppose it's a move to get
us used to paying VAT on take-aways?"

"Gerald went to one and lost three
inches off the thickness of his
wallet."

"Actually I'm sponsored by the
Russian Olympic Boycott
Committee"

"It's good to see two English clubs
in with a chance"

"Remember, the crowd here are *expected* to get up out of their seats"

"If you really want to know,
I'm a plain-clothes Rottweiler"

"Guided tour round all the buildings
saved by the Poet Laureate, sir?"

"And this is our new surrogate mother
range"

"Adam glared at Dinah. Their silence
was like that of a meeting between
Coal Board and N.U.M."

"If it's a pound note, Harvey
don't bother to pick it up"

"Don't believe it, Comrade, it's
probably just a Kremlin in the works"

"Books, books, books…we'll
get fat on *books*"

The cartoons in this collection appeared in *The Times Diary* on the following days:

Front cover:
Thursday February 9 1984

Page v:
Monday December 19 1983

Page 10:
Friday March 22 1983

Page 11:
Friday April 29 1983

Page 12:
Saturday May 7 1983

Page 13:
Thursday May 5 1983

Page 14:
Wednesday May 4 1983

Page 15:
Thursday May 26 1983

Page 16:
Thursday June 9 1983

Page 17:
Wednesday June 15 1983

Page 18:
Tuesday June 28 1983

Page 19:
Thursday July 7 1983

Page 20:
Saturday July 9 1983

Page 21:
Friday July 15 1983

Page 22:
Saturday July 16 1983

Page 23:
Tuesday July 19 1983

Page 24:
Wednesday July 20 1983

Page 25:
Friday July 22 1983

Page 26:
Saturday July 23 1983

Page 27:
Thursday July 28 1983

Page 28:
Friday July 29 1983

Page 29:
Thursday August 4 1983

Page 30:
Thursday August 11 1983

Page 31:
Saturday August 13 1983

Page 32:
Monday August 22 1983

Page 33:
Thursday August 25 1983

Page 34:
Tuesday August 30 1983

Page 35:
Thursday September 1 1983

Page 36:
Saturday September 3 1983

Page 37:
Monday September 5 1983

Page 38:
Friday September 9 1983

Page 39:
Monday September 12 1983

Page 40:
Thursday September 15 1983

Page 41:
Monday September 26 1983